10 by 10

Ten short plays for teens about ethics and values

Conceived and Edited
by
JEFF GOTTESFELD

Playwrights:
José Cruz Gonzáles
Mary Hall Surface
Sandra Fenichel Asher
Barry Kornhauser
Ric Averill
Elizabeth Wong
Caleen Sinnette Jennings
Cherie Bennett
Y York
James DeVita

Dramatic Publishing
Woodstock, Illinois • England • Australia • New Zealand

IMPORTANT BILLING AND CREDIT REQUIREMENTS

All producers of any play in this collection *must* give credit to the playwright and editor in all programs distributed in connection with performances of the play and in all instances in which the title of the play appears for purposes of advertising, publicizing or otherwise exploiting the play and/or a production. The name of the playwright and editor *must* also appear on a separate line, on which no other name appears, immediately following the title, and *must* appear in size of type not less than fifty percent the size of the title type. *In all programs this notice must appear:*

Produced by special arrangement with
THE DRAMATIC PUBLISHING COMPANY of Woodstock, Illinois

10 by 10

CONTENTS

KELSO AND CASE-TEC

By
José Cruz González

For Tia Licha and Vic

* * * * * *

CHARACTERS

KELSO, a boy of 15
CASE-TEC, a boy of 17. Watches over his brother Kelso

SETTING: A bedroom.

TIME: The present. Early night.

Kelso and Case-Tec

AT RISE: *Night. The glow of a television set. KELSO and CASE-TEC sit watching the screen. KELSO surfs the channels by remote. There is no sound coming from the television.*

KELSO. See there he is again.

CASE-TEC. No way.

KELSO. It looks just like him but younger.

CASE-TEC. Go back.

KELSO *(changes the remote)*. See!

CASE-TEC. That's impossible.

KELSO. Dude, I'm telling you it's him.

CASE-TEC. Give it here! *(CASE-TEC takes the remote from KELSO.)*

KELSO. Okay, there he is as an old man with a white beard carrying two stone tablets.

CASE-TEC. He's Moses, right?

KELSO. Here, the apes put him in prison.

CASE-TEC. It's *Planet of the Apes*.

KELSO. I like Marky Mark's version better.

CASE-TEC. Wow, check her out.

KELSO. Who?

CASE-TEC. The babe wearing the bikini in jail with him, stupid.

KELSO. Oh, yeah.

CASE-TEC. And now, he's really old holding a musket over his head smiling like an idiot.

KELSO. Weird.

CASE-TEC. What's his name?

KELSO. I don't know.

CASE-TEC. Who cares? *(The phone rings. They both jump to get it. CASE-TEC grabs it.)* Hello? Yeah, it's me. He's here too. Ah-huh?

KELSO. Let me listen.

CASE-TEC. Shhh! Yeah. Okay. Ah-huh. Ah-huh. Okay. *(CASE-TEC hangs up the phone.)*

KELSO. Well?

CASE-TEC. Nothing's changed.

KELSO. How long do we gotta wait?

CASE-TEC. 'Til something changes.

KELSO. Is Mom going to—

CASE-TEC. I don't know.

KELSO. Did we do the right thing?

CASE-TEC. We had to do it.

KELSO. But what if Pop hadn't—

CASE-TEC. It wouldn't have mattered. He always blows up.

KELSO. What's going to happen to us?

CASE-TEC. Why are you asking so many questions?

KELSO. I just want things the way they were.

CASE-TEC. We're never going back to that house. *(KELSO crosses to the television picking up a game controller.)* What are you doing?

KELSO. I'm playing a video game.

CASE-TEC. Dude, the thing's broken.

KELSO. I know that.

CASE-TEC. Nothing works around here.

KELSO. There's nothing else to do.

CASE-TEC. So you're going to pretend you're playing a game?

KELSO. Go away. *(KELSO pretends to play a video game.)*

CASE-TEC. So what's the game? "Medal of Honor Frontline"?

KELSO. No.

CASE-TEC. "NBA Live"?

KELSO. Yeah, right.

CASE-TEC. "Lord of the Rings"? *(Beat.)* I knew it! It's a dumb game.

KELSO. I always beat you.

CASE-TEC. No you don't.

KELSO. You cry every time.

CASE-TEC. Wanna bet?

KELSO. You're on! *(CASE-TEC sits beside KELSO. They pretend to play. They are very animated pretending to play. CASE-TEC tosses the game controller down.)*

CASE-TEC. I win!

KELSO. No, you cheated.

CASE-TEC. Prove it.

KELSO. I can't.

CASE-TEC. Loser.

KELSO. Cheat. *(KELSO picks up the remote, changing channels again. Beat.)* I'm scared, Case-Tec.

CASE-TEC. I know, Kelso. I am too.

KELSO. Why did Mom do it?

CASE-TEC. She said something made her feel everything was going to be okay.

KELSO. Like what?

CAST-TEC. Like a giant hand protecting us.

KELSO. Do you think she's going to make it out of the hospital?

CASE-TEC. I don't think she can feel a thing right now.

KELSO. He shouldn't have hit her.

CASE-TEC. He was crying like a baby when they took him away.

KELSO. He's going to be mad later.

CASE-TEC. He's never going to lay a hand on us again.

KELSO. Mom led us out of there, didn't she?

CASE-TEC. Yeah, just like that guy in the movie with the stone tablets. *(The phone rings. They both rush to it. CASE-TEC answers it.)* Hello? Yeah? *(CASE-TEC shares the phone so KELSO can hear.)*

KELSO. I'm here.

CASE-TEC. How is she?

KELSO. Is Mom going to be okay?

CASE-TEC. Yes!

KELSO. When can we see her?

CASE-TEC. Soon?

KELSO. I want to go there now.

CASE-TEC. We can't. Yes? Okay. Thanks.

KELSO. 'Bye!

CASE-TEC *(hangs up the phone. He starts to cry)*. You better not tell anybody.

KELSO. I won't.

CASE-TEC. 'Cause if you do—

KELSO. Is Mom going to remember what happened?

CASE-TEC. I hope so.

KELSO. What if she doesn't?

CASE-TEC. Then we gotta tell the truth.

KELSO. Pop's not going to like it.

CASE-TEC. Who cares? It's you, Mom and me. That's all that matters, right?

KELSO. Right.

CASE-TEC. So you wanna play?

KELSO. Nah. You want the remote?

CASE-TEC. Sure. *(CASE-TEC starts surfing the channels.)*

KELSO. Wait!

CASE-TEC. What is it?

KELSO. There he is again.

CASE-TEC. No way!

KELSO. This time he's driving a chariot!

CASE-TEC. That dude's on every channel!

KELSO *(turns off the television)*. Not anymore! *(Beat.)* Case-Tec, are we going to be okay?

CASE-TEC. Yeah, we're going to be okay, Kelso.

(Lights fade to black.)

END OF PLAY

WONDER ON PAPER

By
Mary Hall Surface

CHARACTERS

SHELLY, 14 years old
RUSSELL, 16 years old, Shelly's brother

Two actors are costumed as statues of RA and BASTET, gods of ancient Egypt.

SETTING: The Egyptian gallery of a museum.

TIME: Today.

Wonder on Paper

AT RISE: *SHELLY sits on a bench in the Egyptian gallery of a museum. A statue of the Egyptian sun god, RA, and the cat-goddess BASTET, are the centerpieces of the gallery. Around her on the floor are crumpled sheets of paper. SHELLY sketches furiously in her sketchbook, but flips the pages, starting over and over, then finally rips yet another page and crumples it up, tossing it on the ground. RUSSELL rushes into the gallery.*

RUSSELL *(entering)*. Shel? *(Sees her.)* Great. Got the right gallery. Thought I'd taken a wrong turn at the sphinx. What's up with the litter?

SHELLY *(drawing)*. I'll pick it up. What time is it?

RUSSELL *(checking the clock on his cell phone)*. Three o'clock. Exactly. I had my phone alarm programmed to beep in increasingly smaller intervals, with a mounting sense of urgency.

SHELLY. It can do that?

RUSSELL. Man and machine. We can do anything. Come on, we gotta go!

SHELLY *(drawing)*. Can't.

RUSSELL. We promised Dad in blood we'd taxi back to the hotel by 3:30.

SHELLY. Can't.

RUSSELL *(rapidly picking up SHELLY's discarded drawings, shoving them into her backpack)*. Shelly, if we blow this, our vacation is doomed! They won't let us out of their sight again!

SHELLY. I can't leave until I draw "beauty."

RUSSELL. Do what?

SHELLY. "Beauty." What is it? I want to draw it.

RUSSELL. It's summer, Shel. Honors art class is over.

SHELLY. This is for me! I've spent all day in this museum filled with gorgeous paintings and sculptures that artists have made for thousands of years—

RUSSELL. So draw one of those. *(Checking his clock.)* Quickly!

SHELLY. But they're beautiful *things*—not beauty itself. That's what I want to capture!

RUSSELL. OK. We'll look it up.

SHELLY. What?

RUSSELL *(punching keys on his cell phone)*. Oxford English Dictionary. On-line. Mobile access. Definition: "Beauty."

SHELLY. Russell—

RUSSELL. Shelly. I have the information. The Knowledge.

SHELLY. You have a cell phone.

RUSSELL. I have the Holy Grail of access, a golden bowl of answers. But I can sign off—

SHELLY. Wait! What does it say?

RUSSELL *(reading from his Web access)*. "Beauty: A quality that pleases the mind or senses." There you go. *(SHELLY does not move.)* So draw!

SHELLY. How do you draw that: a "quality"?

RUSSELL. You're an artist, Shel. Figure it out or give it up.

SHELLY. Is that your philosophy of life?

RUSSELL. Excuse me?

SHELLY. Anything you can't figure out, you just don't think about?

RUSSELL. Yes. Exactly! *(Looking at his phone.)* Depleting power bar. Now we really have to go.

SHELLY. Look at this statue.

RUSSELL. Shelly—

SHELLY. I need five minutes. Time me!

RUSSELL *(programming the phone)*. Deal. Four fifty-nine and counting.

SHELLY *(looking at the statue)*. Do you see?

RUSSELL *(reading the label)*. "Egyptian. 2500 B.C. Sandstone. Ra, the sun god." And?

SHELLY. Whoever carved this wanted to know how the sun rises and sets. So he made a god.

RUSSELL. Who sailed in a golden boat across the sky, until sunset. I know all about him. Then he road down into the underworld, and rose again at sunrise. Sunset. Sunrise. But! Science has subsequently explained the actual patterns of the earth's rotation. So that's why this statue is no longer worshiped, but sits in a museum. Can we go now?

SHELLY. But did the artist really believe in Ra or was he trying to do what I'm trying to do?

RUSSELL. I'd call this guy "beast" before I'd call him "beauty."

SHELLY. Stop joking, Russell! Look at this one. She's Ra's daughter, Bastet.

RUSSELL. Who were the first people to keep cats as pets? *(Before SHELLY can answer.)* Egyptians! *(Congratulating himself.)* Score!

SHELLY. She's a goddess!

RUSSELL. Who had the power to ensure a bountiful harvest. The Egyptians had gods for everything—the sky, the earth, the river. So did the Greeks, the Romans, the Aztecs. It's Ancient Cultures 101. Myths. Hello?! To explain why things are the way they are.

SHELLY. But why?

RUSSELL. Why what?

SHELLY. Why do we need to know?

RUSSELL. We're human. We don't like not knowing.

SHELLY. But what if we can never know some things, but we wonder about them anyway.

RUSSELL. Wonder equals confusion. I don't like to be confused.

SHELLY. Mysteries. You like reading mysteries.

RUSSELL. Sure, because you always find out who did it at the end.

SHELLY. So because we're human we take all the big wonders and turn them into stories that we can understand—turn them into statues that look like us?

RUSSELL *(referring to RA)*. I know I've got a bad haircut, but I don't have falcon head and you don't have cat ears!

SHELLY. But we've got arms and legs. Here's all the mystery of how the sun rises and sets, of how things grow reduced down to figures we can recognize.

RUSSELL *(looking at the statues, dubiously)*. Well...

SHELLY. OK, almost recognize. They feel so...small for something so big.

RUSSELL. Shel. The ancient Egyptians just didn't know what we know today.

SHELLY. What *do* we know?

RUSSELL. Everything.

SHELLY. Beauty...mystery...everything?

RUSSELL. Sure.

SHELLY *(looking at her sketch)*. This drawing's not working.

RUSSELL *(deliberately)*. So let's go!

SHELLY *(flips another page)*. Tell me how to do it, Russell.

RUSSELL. Me?! *(RUSSELL's cell phone rings.)* Got to answer this.

SHELLY. Answer *me*!

RUSSELL. Text message. Dad! Oh great!

SHELLY. Stop the clock. *(SHELLY grabs the phone and crosses away from him.)*

RUSSELL. Careful with the technology!

SHELLY *(punching in keys)*. "Dad. Trying to figure out the mystery of the universe. Might take us a minute. Back soon." *(Pushing the off key.)* Off. Here. *(SHELLY tosses the cell phone back to RUSSELL.)*

RUSSELL *(catching it)*. Watch it! You want to break it?

SHELLY. You mean your phone god is not indestructible as well as all-knowing?

RUSSELL. I'd sacrifice small mammals to this thing, OK?

SHELLY. I thought you just said we'd evolved since ancient times.

RUSSELL. You have exactly two minutes before we catch a cab.

SHELLY. But you know everything—

RUSSELL. We made a deal!

SHELLY. Don't you?

RUSSELL *(reactivating the timer)*. Go! *(SHELLY opens her sketchbook again. RUSSELL looks at the statues.)*

SHELLY. Look up God.

RUSSELL. Pardon?

SHELLY. On your phone. Get a definition on-line for God.

RUSSELL. That's too weird.

SHELLY. I'm trying to draw God now.

RUSSELL. What happened to beauty?

SHELLY. Ask it!

RUSSELL. It's a cell phone. Not an oracle!

SHELLY. It's all the wonders of the universe smushed into a little black rectangle, isn't it? Makes the sun rise and set! Worshiped by many, but none more than my brother.

RUSSELL. Oh! You think I'm like the guy who carved these statues—that I've made a god out of a thing.

SHELLY. You've made a god out of having the answers! Of being so sure of yourself that you're afraid! Afraid to wonder about a question that might be too big to answer. Here! *(Shoving the sketchbook toward him.) You* draw beauty…God…everything!

RUSSELL *(snatching the sketchbook)*. Fine. And I *won't* draw my phone! *(RUSSELL sits to draw.)*

SHELLY. You'll draw yourself. *(This lands on RUSSELL. He puts the pencil down.)*

RUSSELL *(genuinely)*. Shelly. I don't know what to draw.

SHELLY. Honest?

RUSSELL. I don't know, OK? Maybe it's…impossible. *(SHELLY crosses and sits next to her brother. She looks at the sketchbook.)*

SHELLY. You did it.

RUSSELL. What? It's blank. There's nothing there.

SHELLY. Or everything's there.

RUSSELL *(liking that idea)*. Huh. You think?

SHELLY. I wonder!

RUSSELL *(acknowledging his sister)*. Yes you do.

SHELLY *(realizing the time)*. We gotta go! *(SHELLY quickly gathers her things. RUSSELL stands, too, but is not so rushed.)*

RUSSELL. See ya, Ra. Bastet.

SHELLY *(to the statues)*. Guess you're beautiful parts of a great big whole. You, too, phone. Full of mystery and power. Maybe nothing can capture the whole. Maybe we shouldn't try.

RUSSELL. Wanna walk back?

SHELLY. Really?

RUSSELL. Sure. Lots to wonder at out there.

SHELLY. Yeah.

(SHELLY and RUSSELL leave the gallery together. RA and BASTET slowly, magically, shift to new positions.)

END OF PLAY

WAITING FOR BOBO

By
SANDRA FENICHEL ASHER

CHARACTERS

DANIELLE, 15 years old
JESSICA, 15 years old

SETTING: Outside of the Savmor One-Stop, a combination
gas station, convenience store, roadside restaurant and
Greyhound bus station in a small Midwestern town. The
store may be represented by a glass door at center. The
door sports a large, brightly colored poster showing a
guitar and boldly proclaiming "Bobo Taylor! One Night
Only!" A smaller sign on the door indicates that this is
an official bus stop and displays the schedule; another
gives the store hours and reads "Closed."

TIME: The present.

Waiting for Bobo

AT RISE: *Past midnight, early spring, and it's turned chilly. DANIELLE is pacing up and down in the parking lot in front of the Savmor. Occasionally, she peers off L, searching the street in vain for signs of Bobo Taylor's tour bus. JESSICA has her back to the audience. She's reading the bus schedule. The door and area in front of it are bathed in eerie after-hours light. JESSICA has a sweater over her shoulders; DANIELLE does not.*

JESSICA. Danielle?

DANIELLE *(impatiently)*. Yeah?

JESSICA. What time is it?

DANIELLE *(holds her wrist up to the light to read her watch)*. One...fifty...seven.

JESSICA. The last bus left at twelve forty-three.

DANIELLE. So?

JESSICA. We should've been on it.

DANIELLE. He'll be here.

JESSICA. Next one's not until 7:09. In the *morning*.

DANIELLE. So we'll be home by eight. No problem.

JESSICA. That's not my point.

DANIELLE. What *is* your point, Jessica?

JESSICA. We may be stuck out here all night.

DANIELLE. He'll be here.

JESSICA. When?

DANIELLE. *Soon.*

JESSICA. The concert ended over two hours ago.

DANIELLE. There's a lot to do after a concert, you know? They have to take down all that equipment, pack everything on the bus...and you saw how many people were trying to talk to him.

JESSICA. If you knew it was going to take so long, why did you tell him to meet us here?

DANIELLE. I thought this place stayed open all night.

JESSICA. Should've read the sign.

DANIELLE. It *looks* like a place that stays open all night!

JESSICA. Who'd come here after the last bus?

DANIELLE. We're here, aren't we?

JESSICA. Oh. Right. *(Muttering to herself.)* The Idiot Patrol.

DANIELLE. I figured it was a good location. Right on the highway. Easy to find.

JESSICA. So why hasn't he found it?

DANIELLE. *He will be here.*

JESSICA *(starts digging around in her purse).* I don't think so.

DANIELLE. What are you doing?

JESSICA. Looking for my cell phone.

DANIELLE. Why?

JESSICA. I'm going to call my mom.

DANIELLE. Jessica! You cannot call your mom!

JESSICA. Oh, no? Watch me.

DANIELLE. What are you going to say to her?

JESSICA. I'm going to ask her to come pick us up, what do you think?

DANIELLE. You told her you were spending the night at my house! I told *my* mom I was spending the night at *your* house! How are you going to explain being *here*?

JESSICA *(after a moment's thought)*. She'll understand.

DANIELLE. Well, my mom will *not*! Do you want to get me grounded for the rest of my life?

JESSICA. No, but I don't want to spend the night in a parking lot, either.

DANIELLE. You promised, Jessica! You *swore* you wouldn't tell.

JESSICA. I know, but it's *creepy* out here. Everything's gone *dark*. And it's getting *cold*!

DANIELLE. You swore to *God*!

JESSICA *(a pause as she considers this—and slowly lets her purse slide to the ground. She plops down beside it)*. I don't know why I stay friends with you.

DANIELLE *(grinning, she sits beside JESSICA, bumping her a little in a teasing way—and also to get closer for warmth. She pulls half of JESSICA's sweater around her own shoulders)*. Because it's fun, that's why.

JESSICA. You get me into more trouble—

DANIELLE. And you love it. You know you do! You loved sneaking out to go to this concert, and you loved talking to Bobo. Admit it!

JESSICA *(nodding)*. It *was* fun. It was cool.

DANIELLE. Yes! And you're going to love being my best friend when I'm a rich and famous country star, touring coast to coast in my very own private bus, *just like Bobo*! *(Beat.)* You can be my manager, if you want.

JESSICA. I don't know anything about that stuff—

DANIELLE. You'll *learn*! We'll *both* learn! That's why I need to *talk* to him—to find out all the stuff we need to know.

JESSICA *(a beat, then, suddenly frowning)*. Danielle?

DANIELLE. Uh-huh?

JESSICA *(another beat, struggles with what's on her mind)*. I don't think he's planning to *talk* to you...exactly.

DANIELLE. What do you mean?

JESSICA. Well, he was...*flirting* with you.

DANIELLE *(pleased with herself)*. Uh-huh. And I was flirting with him, too.

JESSICA *(uncomfortable with this)*. I know.

DANIELLE. That's how you get their attention.

JESSICA. Maybe so, but—

DANIELLE. What are you getting at?

JESSICA. I'm not sure...it's just...been bothering me.

DANIELLE. I am not one of those *groupies*, if that's what you're thinking. I am way too smart for that. That's why it was so important for you to come with me tonight, see? Safety in numbers.

JESSICA. You call being stuck outside a closed Savmor at two o'clock in the morning *safe*?

DANIELLE. We are not *stuck*. We are waiting for Bobo Taylor who said he would meet us here and he *will*.

JESSICA. Why doesn't that make me feel any safer?

DANIELLE. It's perfectly safe! All we're going to do is *talk*—and *maybe* I'll get to *sing* for him!

JESSICA. Here? In a parking lot? In the freezing cold?

DANIELLE. No! He's not going to *walk* over. He'll have his bus.

JESSICA. We're getting on his bus?

DANIELLE. Of course! Don't you want to see the inside of it?

JESSICA. I'm not sure...

DANIELLE. Jessica! It's going to be *fantastic*! You and me on the Bobo Taylor Tour Bus!

JESSICA *(not at all convinced)*. Yeah, well...maybe. But *then* what?

DANIELLE. What do you mean?

JESSICA. After we see the inside of his bus, and we do all this talking, and maybe you get to sing, how do we—get back off? What if he doesn't want us to?

DANIELLE. No problem. We just tell him we're fifteen.

JESSICA. What?

DANIELLE. We're *minors*. He can either give us a lift to Franklin or risk going to jail.

JESSICA *(grabbing her purse and scrambling to her feet)*. That's it. I'm calling my mom.

DANIELLE. You *swore*, Jessica!

JESSICA. I swore not to tell anyone we were catching a bus out of town to go to this concert. I did not swear to stay here all night waiting for Bobo Taylor to show up or not show up or talk to us or not talk to us or kidnap us—or who knows what else! *(Digs frantically in her purse.)*

DANIELLE *(also on her feet now)*. You make that call, and I will never speak to you again as long as I live!

JESSICA. Fine with me.

DANIELLE. *I swear to God!*

JESSICA. I'd watch that if I were you! Better not ask me for a ride when my mom pulls up!

DANIELLE. I *trusted* you, Jessica. I trusted you with my *deepest, most sacred dream*—and you gave your solemn word that you would not tell.

JESSICA. This is your dream—a night in the Savmor parking lot?

DANIELLE. You know that's not what I'm talking about. Bobo Taylor is going to meet us here!

JESSICA. You have gotten us into some bad trouble, Danielle, but this is the worst—whether Bobo Taylor shows up or not! You're crazy, do you know that? You have completely lost your mind!

DANIELLE. I am *not* crazy. I'm going to be a *star*, and I am willing to do whatever it takes.

JESSICA. That's *exactly* what I'm afraid of! *(As DANIELLE turns away angrily.)* You know what I think?

DANIELLE *(muttering)*. Who cares?

JESSICA. I think it's lucky for you he *hasn't* shown up.

DANIELLE *(looks up the street, beginning to have doubts)*. He said he'd be here.

JESSICA. He said a lot of things...

DANIELLE. And he meant them!

JESSICA. Oh, yeah? So why was he laughing?

DANIELLE. *He meant what he said!*

JESSICA. He was *laughing* at us, Danielle. He was laughing at *you*!

DANIELLE. You said he was flirting—

JESSICA. Flirting, laughing, it's all the same. Don't you think he has someone just like you at every stop on the tour? One Danielle Johnson after another, all wanting their big break, all willing to do whatever it takes, if only he'll sprinkle some magic fairy dust on their stupid little heads and make it happen.

DANIELLE. He *said* he would *meet us*—

JESSICA. And how many others did he say that to? All he has to do is keep on saying it—and then take the best offer! Next morning, he's five hundred miles away. *(She pulls out her cell phone and jabs at the "on" button angrily.)*

DANIELLE. That is so *cruel…*

JESSICA. Yeah, well, the truth hurts. *(A few more jabs at the button, then she stops trying.)* Ah, *crap*!

DANIELLE. What?

JESSICA. My battery's dead. Do you have your phone?

DANIELLE. Wouldn't give it to you if I did.

JESSICA *(no nonsense)*. *Do you have your phone?*

DANIELLE. No.

JESSICA. You didn't bring your cell phone?

DANIELLE. I didn't want my mom calling me on it.

JESSICA. *What are we going to do?*

DANIELLE *(shrugs, gives up, sits on ground)*. Nothing. Might as well sit down.

JESSICA *(not sitting)*. Crap!

DANIELLE *(a beat, then, chagrined)*. Jess?

JESSICA *(snapping)*. What?

DANIELLE. He's not coming, is he? *(JESSICA rolls her eyes, looks away. A beat, then—)* I'm cold. *(JESSICA heaves an impatient sigh. Another beat, then—)* And I'm sorry.

JESSICA *(groans, then turns to face DANIELLE)*. Yeah. Well. *(A beat, then sitting beside her.)* What time is it?

DANIELLE *(checks her watch)*. Two-oh-six. *(JESSICA nods slowly. They look at one another, DANIELLE crestfallen, and JESSICA disgusted.)* It could be worse. It could be raining.

JESSICA. Yeah. And we could be struck by lightning.

DANIELLE *(slyly).* Only if you'd made that call to your mom.

(A beat. then JESSICA shakes her head, gives up, and tosses half her sweater around DANIELLE's shoulders. They break out in grins and huddle together as lights fade.)

END OF PLAY

LAST MINUTE

By
BARRY KORNHAUSER

For David and Lee

* * * * * *

CHARACTERS

NARRATOR, female
ELECTRIC GUITAR PLAYER, female
ELECTRIC BASSIST, male
DRUMMER, male

The three actors portraying the musicians each need to be able to play sixty seconds of a hard-rock sound (although not necessarily well). This same minute of music is repeated in various permutations throughout the scenes. If that cannot be accomplished, it is possible for the sound to be pre-recorded with the actors miming the action of playing their instruments.

SETTING: A stage.

TIME: Seven minutes from Now.

Last Minute

AT RISE: *A dimly lit stage. Lingering UC is a heavy-metal teen band comprised of a female ELECTRIC GUITAR PLAYER, male ELECTRIC BASSIST and male DRUMMER. Once they begin playing, their music should have a sound* Rolling Stone *magazine once described as "dinosaurs eating cars." Over the musicians' heads, across the width of the stage, hangs a single string of unlit Christmas lights. Downstage to one side, the set model of this production sits on a podium. Other than this, the stage is bare, void of any apparent design—all of which is replicated on the model, of course. A teenage female NARRATOR, carrying a clipboard and wearing a stopwatch around her neck, enters opposite the podium.*

SCENE 1

NARRATOR *(starting the watch; addressing the audience).* One. *(After assuring that the watch is running, she turns her attentions to the clipboard's checklist, and calls.)* House up! *(The houselights turn on. The NARRATOR makes an affirmative checkmark on the clipboard list.)* House out! *(The houselights turn off again. The NARRATOR marks another check.)* Works, please! *(The stage brightens in a bland wash of work light. Another check.)* Works out! *(The stage dims even more darkly than before. Check again.)* Dimmer check! *(A pin spot comes up on the NARRATOR who makes another mark of approval.)* Next! *(A light comes up on the band. The GUITAR PLAYER begins a solo. Pleased, the NARRATOR makes another mark.)* Next! *(A special comes up on the set model. The NARRATOR looks at it, then the rest of the lit stage, and lastly into the darkened house. She makes her check, then lowers the clipboard.)* Good! *(She crosses to the model, the spotlight following her, places the clipboard inside the podium, and again addresses the audience.)* In theater, an important tool of the scenic designer is the set model. *(A brief but distinctive guitar flourish serves as a "fanfare.")* On this model of our set, built to scale, one inch equals one foot. If this play were to have a temporal model, one minute would equal one day. *(The NARRATOR looks at her watch. When sixty seconds have passed, she stops it.)* Time!

(The GUITAR PLAYER stops.)

SCENE 2

NARRATOR *(starting the watch).* Two. *(A drum solo begins.)* In attempting to accomplish the task of interpreting the Word on the page as Action on the stage, we struggle to render in performance the text's very atmosphere *(reaching into the podium, she produces an aerosol air freshener which she then sprays over the stage)* and also to actively engage you, the audience, in the process. *(She produces a Super-Soaker and sprays it across the audience. After a good squirting, the NARRATOR puts the water toy away and looks once again at her watch. When sixty seconds have passed, she clicks it off.)* Time!

(The DRUMMER stops.)

SCENE 3

NARRATOR *(starting the watch).* Three. *(The BASSIST begins his solo. The NARRATOR removes a large flowerpot and places it on the podium, then loads it with a few spadefuls of dirt also drawn from inside the podium. She plants a seed in that soil and then starts to cross the stage with the flowerpot. As she does so, she also begins speaking.)* In the building of this piece... *(She exits, but immediately reenters, crossing opposite and carrying what appears to be the same flowerpot, only now a small plant is growing in its soil. She continues speaking as she does so.)* ...we have worked slavishly... *(She exits again and instantly reenters with the plant, which has now grown considerably. In fact, it is so large it is cumbersome to carry. Once again, she continues as she crosses.)* ...to assemble and/or construct... *(She exits one last time, only to return right away, this time pulling a rope tied to a wheeled platform upon which sits that same flowerpot—now containing a young tree! One apple grows on its leafy branches. As she maneuvers the cart into position, she finishes her speech.)* ...production elements that are both utilitarian and aesthetically apt. *(She readjusts the tree's position until satisfied and then looks at her watch. When sixty seconds have passed, she stops it.)* Time!

(The BASSIST stops.)

SCENE 4

NARRATOR *(starting the watch)*. Four. *(The GUITAR
    PLAYER and DRUMMER begin playing together.)* Other
    elements of design demanded our attention and energies.
    Good lighting, for example, does more than simply illu-
    minate the stage; it illuminates ideas, evokes mood and
    defines space. *(The GUITAR PLAYER and DRUMMER
    briefly stop and, with choreographed precision, don
    coal-mining hard hats—preferably one painted light
    blue, the other black—and switch on their lights. They
    then resume playing. But they stop again after only a
    few moments; something is aesthetically wrong. The
    NARRATOR plugs two extension cords together and the
    string of Christmas lights hanging above them illumi-
    nates. Satisfied, the two musicians carry on. The NAR-
    RATOR looks at her watch. When sixty seconds have
    passed, she clicks it off.)* Time!

(The GUITAR PLAYER and DRUMMER stop.)

SCENE 5

NARRATOR *(starting the watch)*. Five. *(The DRUMMER
    and the BASSIST now play together.)* Whether couched
    in metaphor or the fiction of reality, the play's story is
    ours to communicate. Yet somehow, I fear, in the stress
    and frenzy of trying to tell this story in ten minutes or
    less—

ALL THREE BAND MEMBERS *(as DRUMMER and BASSIST stop playing)*. And not as a monologue!

(The two musicians resume the music as the GUITAR PLAYER exits.)

NARRATOR. —we may have lost sight of the very reason we tread these boards in the first place. Caught up in our furious labors to build this stage world, we neglect to stop and appreciate its beauty and the true marvel of its creation—

(The GUITAR PLAYER reenters with everybody's lunch.)

GUITAR PLAYER. Sandwiches are here! Who ordered the fish? Who ordered the chicken? *(The NARRATOR awkwardly raises her hand. As the GUITAR PLAYER starts crossing to her.)* Both?

NARRATOR. This is hard work. *(Shaking her head, the GUITAR PLAYER plops a large bag into the NARRATOR's hands and then brings the other band members their lunches. The NARRATOR looks inside her bag.)* Hey, you forgot the milk! *(The GUITAR PLAYER gives her a look and exits again.)* As I was saying, we sometimes fail to remember that the medium of theater—although it has tipped many a sacred cow—had its antecedents in worship, in the religious rituals of the ancient world... So how can we come to honor those origins, how do we make our art "holy" again?

(The GUITAR PLAYER reenters either wearing a cow mask or operating a cow puppet. However one chooses to play it, this creature bears a sign reading "HOLY COW.")

GUITAR PLAYER *(in the guise of the HOLY COW, to the NARRATOR)*. A fan once asked a great musician how he handled the notes so well. The man answered: "The notes I handle no better than many musicians. But the *pauses* between the notes—ah! that's where the art resides. *Udder*ly." Sorry, they're out of milk. But went for more. Promised to send one up in a minute.

NARRATOR *(looking at her stopwatch and indicating her lunch)*. That's fine; it's too early anyway.

GUITAR PLAYER. Early!?

(The NARRATOR nods, showing her the face of the stopwatch. The GUITAR PLAYER looks at the audience and drops the COW guise.)

NARRATOR *(handing her a ten-dollar bill)*. Here, keep the change. *(Her spirits revived, the GUITAR PLAYER gestures her appreciation for the tip and begins to cross back to the band area, as the NARRATOR again turns her attentions to the watch, stopping it, as always, after sixty seconds have passed. She takes a noticeable pause before saying.)* Moo. Sorry—Time.

(The DRUMMER and BASSIST stop.)

SCENE 6

NARRATOR *(starting the watch)*. Six. *(Now all three musicians begin playing together. Through the course of the scene their music gradually increases in volume until it becomes almost uncomfortable to hear.)* We actors *(she indicates herself and then the others who stop and bow, and then continue their music)*, strangers to one another only a few weeks ago, have become "family," united by our shared responsibility of imbuing life into our dramatis personae, what you know better as a play's—Characters.

(From out of the podium, the NARRATOR dramatically reveals a Barbie doll and a G.I. Joe [or similar action figure], displaying them prominently to the audience.)

BASSIST. Hey!

(He stamps forward and grabs his G.I. Joe, taking it back to his place. Then, very sheepishly, the male DRUMMER runs downstage and grabs his Barbie, taking it back to the drum set. Needing replacements, the NARRATOR crosses into the house and brings one male and one female audience member on stage. She plucks the apple from the tree and hands it to the female "volunteer." She then engages in dialogue with both, but the words cannot be heard by the audience, as they are drowned out by the increasingly earsplitting music. Finally, the NARRATOR looks at her stopwatch. And when sixty seconds have passed...)

NARRATOR & the TWO VOLUNTEERS. TIME!!!

(The musicians all stop.)

SCENE 7

(The silence is palpable and it is heavenly. It gives the NARRATOR a new idea, an inspiration. Hiding her hands from the band, she holds up seven fingers for the audience to see, while mouthing the word "Seven." The band members are silent, awaiting their verbal cue. None comes. As they begin to grow a bit edgy, the NARRATOR silently releases the two "volunteers" back to their seats with a "thank-you" handshake. She then closes her eyes and deeply breathes in the divine stillness. The band members, however, are becoming more and more anxious. Finally, after a good thirty seconds of this...)

BASSIST *(whispering to the others)*. Can someone tell me what the heck is going on?

GUITAR PLAYER *(whispering back)*. Nothing! It's the final scene of the play and absolutely *nothing* is going on!

DRUMMER *(also whispering)*. It must be some last-minute change [name of actress playing NARRATOR] concocted.

BASSIST *(still whispering)*. Is that "kosher"?

(The others shrug in reply.)

GUITAR PLAYER *(calling out to the NARRATOR)*. Hey, [name of actress], you sure this is dramaturgically sound?

DRUMMER. Yeah, I mean, really—

ALL MUSICIANS. —just what kind of an ending do you call this?!

NARRATOR *(taking her time; slowly opening her eyes, facing the audience)*. "Perfect." ...Time.

(She smiles. Blackout.)

END OF PLAY

SITTING WITH BERTIE

By
RIC AVERILL

CHARACTERS

WILL
MOM
DAD
LIZ

SETTING: The action takes place in three areas: One—a kitchen table with four chairs, Two—several chairs arranged to look like a "bus" and Three—a pool of light on the other side of the bus representing "Day Camp."

TIME: Summer.

Sitting With Bertie

AT RISE: *Lights come up on area One. DAD is reading a Civil War magazine and MOM is chopping some vegetables. WILL enters, flopping down a fish wrapped in newspaper. MOM opens it up, grimaces slightly.*

WILL. I really caught two, but the other got away. *(DAD smiles and nods.)*

MOM. I'll fry it up if you like.

DAD. Bones and all it's at least twelve ounces—camp record?

WILL. My first fish this summer, Pops—so I suppose that makes it a record.

DAD. Catch two tomorrow, set a new one.

WILL *(in DAD's face)*. I'd be better if you'd ever taken me fishing as a kid.

DAD. You are a kid. And I paid for camp.

MOM. *We* paid for camp?

DAD *(smiles at her)*. That's true, so true. *(To WILL.)* You man enough to scale it?

WILL. We did the gross stuff at the dock—slit it, gutted it and washed it off with the hose. I'm gonna dry the scales and hot-glue them to Iggy.

MOM. In the garage. Dry them in the house and it'll smell worse than Libby's diapers.

WILL. No. Nothing smells worse—

DAD. Iggy will be the world's first fish-a-saurus.

WILL. He's a dragon, Dad, not a dinosaur. Dragons have scales. You had no childhood.

MOM *(handing DAD a piece of carrot)*. He's still in it.

DAD. Ah, I forgot the progression—you give up dinosaurs when you notice girls and… *(Looks at MOM.)* you don't need dragons once you're married.

WILL *(pause)*. I wanna take two Fishing sessions tomorrow. Will you write me a note?

MOM. What would you have to miss?

WILL. Just Horsemanship.

DAD. You love Horsemanship. I'm making a trophy case for all your badges.

WILL. If I catch three fish we can all have one for dinner tomorrow. Please.

DAD *(looks up at MOM)*. Just follow the normal rotation. It can't hurt to do what the counselors expect.

WILL. Maybe I don't even want to go.

DAD *(looks up from magazine)*. Really. *(Pause.)* What's going on? Horses bite or something.

WILL. No. It's just fishing's more fun.

DAD. More fun. And?

WILL. Paul Kahn isn't there.

DAD. Don't let him give you any trouble this year.

WILL. Too late. Him being there is trouble.

MOM. What about Liz? She'll be riding, won't she?

WILL. She's hardly talking to me. Will you just write the note?

DAD *(looks at MOM, they come to a silent agreement)*. Just stay in the rotation and I'll take you fishing Sunday.

Really—borrow Uncle Tom's gear. Promise. *(WILL thinks for a minute, looks up, nods reluctantly.)*

MOM. Give it one more day.

WILL. I suppose. *(WILL walks over to area Three—"Day Camp"—where LIZ walks into the scene.)* Hey, Liz, walk you to Fishing?

LIZ *(a little surprised, looks around).* Will. No, I mean, uh, I'm not going. I'm taking double Horsemanship. *(Holds up a note.)* Dad wrote me a note.

WILL. Why?

LIZ. Fish smell.

WILL. Horses don't?

LIZ *(looks around).* Look, I gotta go. I don't want to be late. *(Starts to leave.)*

WILL *(stops her with his voice).* For Paul? What's he been saying about me?

LIZ. Nothing, I don't know. *(Pause.)* I guess you just gotta think a little before you pick your friends.

WILL *(slightly sarcastic).* Yeah, well I'm sure Paul's a fine friend.

LIZ. Look, I'll see you at Youth Group, OK? Just not here. I really gotta go. *(She leaves. He kicks the ground.)*

WILL. Stupid. *(He walks to area One—the kitchen.)* Stupid, stupid, stupid me.

(MOM is standing, arms crossed. DAD is seated, doodling with a pen. WILL sits across from him.)

MOM. A fight. That's just not like you.

WILL. Is today.

DAD. Don't take that tone with your mother.

WILL. Sorry, can I go?

DAD. Not just yet. *(Pause.)* Who started it?

WILL. Does it matter? *(Pause.)*

DAD. No. I was just sort of hoping...

WILL. I didn't really fight. I got fought. Only after getting hit a couple of times, I stepped out of the way and Paul ended up in the water. *(DAD fights back a small laugh.)*

MOM. Did you tell that to the counselors?

WILL. It doesn't matter. A fight's a fight. Anyway, Paul's like, the most popular kid at camp. If I...we both lost canteen privileges for two days. The word is out it's my fault.

DAD. But it isn't.

WILL. Well, it kind of is.

MOM. I don't like to hear you talk like that...it's victim mentality.

WILL. It's "I'm-not-going-back-to-camp" mentality. I'll pay you back the registration fee.

DAD. Will, you've done two or three sessions of day camp every summer since you were nine.

MOM. Eight. We lied about your age the first year.

WILL *(looks up at them, then to DAD)*. You ever get in a fight?

DAD. With my brothers. Usually pillows—though once I threw a spaceship at Tom and he ended up with three stitches.

MOM. Maybe that's why he always cooks us spicy food.

WILL. What'd he do to make you so mad?

DAD. I don't remember now. Maybe he had something I wanted. Maybe because he was a year older. Maybe I was jealous 'cause he wore crutches at the time and got lots of attention.

WILL. Like when Grandpa carried him the whole three-hour tour of Carlsbad Caverns?

DAD *(smiles)*. No, I don't think I was jealous of that. I always thought that just said a lot about Grandpa. *(Smiles sadly at MOM.)*

WILL. You're a good dad, too. *(Looks at MOM.)* I'm sorry, Mom.

MOM *(pats his head)*. So you'll go to camp?

WILL. Sorry about Grandpa. Not about camp. I can't go back—especially now. Practically everybody hates me.

DAD. So don't hang out with practically everybody. Hang out with your friends.

WILL. I don't have any.

DAD. Come on, Will. The fight'll be yesterday's news. Things will get better.

WILL. It was a fight, Dad. With the most popular kid at camp. Things won't get better if I go back. How'd you like it if I came home tomorrow and told you I gave *Paul* three stitches?

MOM *(starts to relent)*. Maybe—

DAD. Wait a minute. I'll make you a deal, Will. You tell us exactly what happened, and we'll listen—then we'll all decide about camp. *(MOM sits down. WILL nods slowly, then stands up to tell the story, sometimes near the second "bus" area, sometimes back to the table, illustrating.)*

WILL. There's this girl, Bertie—the name's bad enough—but she's a "newbie," and Monday, she wet her pants. I mean, you could smell it—and see it. So Tuesday, Paul and a bunch of the others started teasing her and calling her "piss-pot" and "baby." Nobody would do anything with her or walk with her. Then she did it again—just after lunch. The teasing got worse. I saw her at snack time sitting at the pavilion, by herself, staring at the lake—like she wished she could be in it and no one would know. *(He sighs, now walking toward the "bus," placing BERTIE in a seat.)* So on the ride home—she was alone, toward the back, and I walked past everyone and—I sat by her. She didn't talk much. I think she's special, you know, lives in kind of a different world. But she smiled once. No one else did. Now *I* might as well live in a different world.

MOM. That's very sweet, Will.

WILL. Sweet doesn't make you friends.

DAD. You made *one*.

WILL. I suppose.

DAD. And what made you do it?

WILL. You. You and Mom. I thought it's what you'd want me to do—you know, stand up for people and stuff.

DAD *(smiles)*. You're a good kid, Will. Better than I was at your age. We had a slow kid in class we all picked on, Roger Tamblyn—used to tease him and get him to fetch things for us.

WILL. But I thought…

DAD. I was more like Paul at your age than you, I'm afraid. Politics, religion, caring—the stuff we try to share with you—all that comes with a great deal of experience and a few mistakes. I'm really proud of you.

MOM. Me too. I'm sorry some of your friends don't understand—but maybe they're not the friends you really want to have. Why they act the way they do, I don't know. But you acted out of love—

WILL. I don't love her.

MOM. The real kind of love, Will, compassion for other people—the kind that makes a difference.

DAD. What the others think doesn't matter. You know, I'll bet half of them don't even really feel the way they're acting. What's important is how you feel about it—how you feel about yourself.

WILL. I feel OK, now. So, I did right?

DAD. Yeah.

MOM. You did right.

WILL *(pause, smiles)*. So, I guess I gotta go to camp again tomorrow.

DAD. Only if you want to.

(MOM and DAD stand and walk off. WILL takes a deep breath and goes to sit in area Two, on the "bus." He is smiling a little, keeping to himself. LIZ walks on, looks around, then sits down beside him.)

LIZ. Anyone sitting here?

WILL *(looks at her directly)*. How come you're not sitting by Paul?

LIZ. I saw you sitting with Bertie at lunch again today. I saw her smile. And I thought, "Liz, I guess you just gotta think a little before you pick your friends."

WILL. Just don't pee your pants, OK? *(She laughs.)*

END OF PLAY

"QUICK-DRAW GRANDMA"

By
ELIZABETH WONG

CHARACTERS

GRANDMA, 80s, a white-haired, sweet-faced bubbeh/abuelita/nen nen/nonna/nanna/oma. She can be Jewish or Mexican or Chinese or Italian or German. In other words, Granny was born elsewhere. English is her second language.

KEVIN, 13 years old, a kindhearted kid with a logical mind, born here in the United States to first-generation American parents. His idol is extreme pro-skater Tony Hawk, and he dreams about doing scary tricks on his skateboard. He uses the word "Grandma" and its language equivalent interchangeably.

SETTING: On the porch, on the stoop, or a backyard patio, USA.

TIME: A hot summer day.

NOTES

Costumes should be contemporary, not cartoon-y. Do not costume for ethnicity or ethnic origin. No babushka attire for Granny! Imaginary flies are best, suggested by the sound of buzzing. Props: (minimal to none), except a skateboard, jar of flies and an accordion-style handheld Asian fan.

ACKNOWLEDGMENTS

Special thanks to my three goofy nephews Alex, Kevin and Steven for the jokes; my brother William and Nen Nen Grandma for inspiration and guidance; also to the brilliant Jeff Gottesfeld; the lovely Cherie Bennett; to Popo in heaven, and the ever-supportive Gayle Sergel of Dramatic Publishing.

"Quick-Draw Grandma"

AT RISE: *GRANDMA, sitting on a low stool. She finds relief from the summer heat by cooling herself with a pretty fan.*

GRANDMA. Two eighty-one. Two eighty-one. Two eighty-one. *(Loud buzzing from an unseen black fly.)* Two eighty-one. Two eighteeeeeeeee... *(Suddenly, she snaps shut the fan, and WHAM!!! This fly is finito.)* Two. Two eighty-two. *(She flicks the unseen fly into a jar black with its dead brethren.)* Two eighty-two. Two eighteeeeeee... *(Multiple buzzing. With her eyes, GRANDMA tracks three separate flies zipping around in a complicated trajectory. Suddenly, she wields her deadly fan! BAM! BAM! And...BAM! GRANDMA, pointing to each carcass.)* Three, four, and FIVE!

(Seated or standing, GRANDMA does a delightful butt-wiggling victory dance. KEVIN enters, riding a skateboard.)

KEVIN *(overlapping)*. FIVE-forty varial McTwist from the vert, takes big air, the crowd goes wild, land the revert with awesome style, yaaaaay. And, for the grand finale, I bust a 360 one-wheel one-handed handstand! *(Beat.)*

Awright! *(He hops off his skateboard. To GRANDMA.)* Waaaaaaassup, "Gee." *(GRANDMA holds up her jar, shakes it. KEVIN peers into jar.)* Whoa. That is a whole lot of dead flies. How many you got?

GRANDMA. Two hundred eighty-five, and counting.

KEVIN. Whoa, Grandma Bin Laden. What's up with the mass extermination?

GRANDMA. I don't like the way they think.

KEVIN. Whoa. *(Beat.)* Huh?

GRANDMA. The mind of a fly works like the mind of the criminal. They sneak like a thief into your house. They fly everywhere, land on everything, create crazy chaos!

KEVIN. Okaaaay. *(Beat.)* I don't get it.

GRANDMA. Come, my Kevin. Come look. Closer. Closer. Close enough.

KEVIN *(looks at a fly on the ground).* Little dude is just chillin'.

GRANDMA. See how he's rubbing his hands. Like this. *(She demonstrates the movements of a fly with reasonable facsimile.)* Do you know why? Because first, they load up on rotting stinking rotting garbage, and then, over there, they see fresh steaming doggie doo, oh ho, let's go land on it. So they rub rub rub rub, clean clean clean all that disgusting doggie doodoo right into your dinner.

KEVIN. Grosssssssss, Grandma.

GRANDMA. That's nothing. When I was your age, in the old country, because we were soooooo hungry, we had to eat food even though there were flies in it, big dead flies and some even still wiggling. In order to survive, we had to eat flies.

KEVIN. Grossssssss. So that's why you kill flies?

GRANDMA *(in her native language).* I *hate* flies. *(In English.)* I hate them, so I kill them.

KEVIN. When you put it that way, it's like you have a reason to hate flies. Like revenge of the killer grandma. If you hate 'em, you can kill 'em. *(To the fly on ground.)* You're born, you fly, you die. *(Beat.)* Whoa, there it goes. *(Crazy buzzing is heard.)*

GRANDMA *(in her native language).* Kevin, move your butt! *(In English.)* Give Grandma some working room! *(GRANDMA indicates the square footage within her arm's reach.)*

KEVIN. Oh, sorry. My bad. I'm in your strike zone. *(KEVIN takes one step to the side. She motions for him to take another step, and another, and also one step back. Suddenly, she swipes the air with her hand and then holds out her fist.)*

GRANDMA. Yes or no?

KEVIN. No way. I say, no.

GRANDMA. Listen. *(She holds her closed fist to his ear.)*

KEVIN *(eyes widening).* Bitchin'! I mean, wow, that's off the hook, ninja Grandma! How'd you do that?

GRANDMA. The trick is, grab it from behind. But you have to be quick. Then, you slowly close your hand tight around the fly. Then, you wiggle the fly under your thumb. And then, you roll it against all four fingers. Until it suffocates.

KEVIN. Cool.

GRANDMA. Killing a fly this way is bitchin'. But if you feel the fly juices, it means you squeezed a little too hard. *(Beat.)* Want to practice?

KEVIN. No way.

GRANDMA. It's not dead yet.

KEVIN. Grandma, I know you hate flies because you had to eat 'em. But that was a long time ago. And, well, you are hanging out here, for hours, and well, these flies are not even sitting in your dinner or inside the house creating chaos.

GRANDMA. Well, it's fun.

KEVIN. You are killing innocent flies because it's fun.

GRANDMA. Kevin, my grandson, who's side are you on?

KEVIN. Your side, Grandma. I'm on your side. But, killing for fun is kinda sick. You are so busted, Grandma.

GRANDMA. Okay. I admit, I am a murderer of flies. Many flies I have executed. Just because it's fun to sit here on a nice summer day. But they deserve to die, don't you think? Flies are dirty, nasty and useless.

KEVIN. Well, if it turns out that even the life of a fly is valuable and useful, would you stop killing them?

GRANDMA. Maybe. Maybe not.

KEVIN. Well, I'm no big fan of the fly. But know what? Flies *are* kinda useful. We learned in school, frogs and fish and other animals eat 'em for food. They are part of the food chain. So, Grandma, that makes them useful. Oh, and they help out in something called decomposition. Because they lay these eggs see, that turn into these white worms called maggots, and these worms eat dead things, or else we'd be up to our necks in junk and dead stuff.

GRANDMA. Uh-huh.

KEVIN. And those flies you had to eat when you were a kid, maybe by eating them, they kept you alive. You are alive today because you ate flies.

GRANDMA *(holds out her closed hand)*. Want to kill it?

KEVIN. No, Grandma, I don't want to kill it. I don't hate flies.

GRANDMA. Open your hand. Come on.

KEVIN. Let it go, Grandma. I mean, I'm no big fan of the fly. But it was just buzzing along, minding its own business, doing its own thing. Maybe this one was going home, to see his fly mom or his fly dad. Maybe this fly has a grandma, who was waiting up for him all night long, and you just snatched him out of the sky. Now he won't ever get home to see Grandma.

GRANDMA. Oh. I never thought of it that way. *(Beat.)* But, they are fun to catch and squish.

KEVIN. Get a new hobby, Grandma.

GRANDMA *(after a thoughtful moment, finally decides).* Kevin, my grandson, you have a good heart. *(To fly in hand.)* Excuse me. My apologies. You are free. *(GRANDMA slowly opens her hand. They watch the unseen fly as it buzzes along its very wobbly and woozy trajectory.)* Okay, my Kevin, time for dinner.

KEVIN. Grrrreat. But don't forget to wash your hands, *awright? [As they walk off, GRANDMA puts her arm around KEVIN's shoulder. But before they exit, GRANDMA deliberately wipes her hands on KEVIN's back.)*

GRANDMA *(off his expression, feign innocence).* Whaaaat?! *(She wipes her hands on his back again.)*

KEVIN. Funny, Grandma, very funny. So what's for dinner?

GRANDMA. Since you like them sooooo much: barbecued flies.

KEVIN. Funny, Grandma, very funny. You are kidding, right?

(They exit. Blackout.)

END OF PLAY

GROWN UP TREE

By
CALEEN SINNETTE JENNINGS

CHARACTERS

BITTY, age 11 (played by a girl 11-13)
BILLY, age 16 (played by a boy 16-18)
BETH, 40 (played by a woman 35-45)

SETTING: An oak tree dominates the stage. It has a thick
   trunk and roots deep into the ground. It looks embracing
   and menacing at the same time. On the ground beneath
   the tree is a rumpled sheet.

TIME: The early 1960s.

Grown Up Tree

AT RISE: *BITTY sits on the sheet rubbing her arm. She catches a glimpse of a gold wedding band, grabs it and holds it up to the light. BETH runs in from R, still looking over her shoulder at someone offstage. She is breathless and disheveled. BITTY quickly hides the ring in her pocket and rubs her arm again.*

BETH. Is it broken, Bitty? Let me see?

BITTY. It's just sore. *(BETH checks BITTY for broken bones, BITTY eases away.)* I'm all right, Mama.

BETH. Get off the sheet. *(BETH pulls the sheet out from under BITTY and bundles it up.)* Why aren't you in school?

BITTY. Half day. *(Pointing offstage R.)* Who's that, Mama?

BETH. I'm calling the school so you'd better be telling the truth. *(BETH starts to exit. BITTY grabs her arm and points offstage R.)*

BITTY. Who's that man running?

BETH. I ought to spank you for sitting up there.

BITTY. I like being up in my tree. Daddy promised to make me a swing, but he didn't.

BETH. Maybe he'll make it when he gets better.

BITTY. Is he gonna die?

BETH. Hush now, Bitty. Come in the house.

BITTY. The sky's mad today.

BETH. It's gonna rain.

BITTY. Who was that man?

BETH. Nobody.

BITTY. Mr. Nobody?

BETH. Look, Bitty... It was nothing. We were just talking. *(Starting to exit.)* Now come on in. You're just getting over a cold.

BITTY. You kissed him.

BETH. No, honey, I...

BITTY. I saw you. You kissed him and then he... *(BETH puts her hand gently over BITTY's mouth. Then she smooths BITTY's hair and hugs her.)* If you hadn't screamed, I wouldn't have fallen out of my tree.

BETH. I'm sorry. I was surprised to see a face in the branches.

BITTY. I was surprised when you and Mr. Nobody found my secret tree.

BETH. Let's forget about it, okay? *(BETH glances at her left hand and jumps. She spreads out the sheet and looks, then she searches the ground all around the tree.)*

BITTY. What's wrong?

BETH. Nothing. Go inside now.

BITTY. I love Daddy.

BETH. I know, honey.

BITTY. Do you love Daddy?

BETH *(continues searching the ground)*. Yes.

BITTY. Then why did you kiss Mr. Nobody?

BETH. Mama can't talk about this now, Bitty-baby.

BITTY. Don't call me that! I'm not a baby!

BETH. I'm sorry. You're Bitty-Big Girl, okay?

BITTY *(cries in frustration)*. I've got underarm hair, and leg hair, and I got a boyfriend named Raymond Branch, and he's gonna marry me, and he kissed me too, nicer than Mr. Nobody! *(BETH, startled by the outburst, hands BITTY a handkerchief.)*

BETH. Bitty, please don't cry. Blow your nose. I know you're upset. I'm sorry. Hush now. *(She drops to her hands and knees to search again.)*

BITTY. What are you looking for?

BETH. Nothing.

BITTY. Maybe Mr. Nobody took your nothing. *(BITTY stretches out her arms and circles around the tree. BETH searches the ground but occasionally glances at BITTY.)*

BETH. Have you seen my ring?

BITTY *(chanting as she circles her tree)*.

What you doing?

I don't know.

Ring around my tree I go.

Daddy says my tree has rings, and every ring tells you what happened to my tree each year it was alive—if it had too much rain, if it was thirsty, if it got hit by lightning. The rings tell me secrets. I'm making rings around the rings. *(BITTY makes circles around the tree as she chants.)*

Ring around my big oak tree

Who is going to marry me?

BETH. Help me look for my ring, Bitty. Please? *(BITTY joins BETH on her knees. BETH searches, BITTY talks.)*

Promise not to say anything about what you saw.

BITTY. 'Cause you'll get in trouble?

BETH. You don't want to hurt Daddy, do you?

BITTY. I'm not the one who kissed Mr. Nobody and lost my ring. *(Pause.)*

BETH. Who's Raymond Branch?

BITTY. My boyfriend.

BETH. You're too young for that.

BITTY. Raymond *Branch*, isn't that funny? When he kissed me, my head went round in circles.

BETH. You're too young to kiss boys.

BITTY *(jumping up and circling the tree).*

> Will he catch me?
>
> He's too slow
>
> Ring around my tree I go.

BETH *(stands and gently takes BITTY by the shoulders).* I guess what you saw makes you more of an adult than a little girl. We have adult secrets between us, Bitty. You won't tell Daddy what you saw, and I won't tell Daddy about Raymond. But no more kissing, do you understand? If you have underarm hair and leg hair and all that, you know what I'm talking about. Just because you're growing up, and we can share secrets, that doesn't mean I'm going to stop being your mama. No more kissing. You will mind me, Bitty. You hear?

BITTY. Yes, ma'am.

BETH. Swear to me. If you want me to trust you like an adult, you have to swear on something you love. Swear on your tree. Go on.

BITTY *(kneels in front of the tree).*

> I get on my knee
>
> And swear on my tree
>
> For all the world to see.

(BITTY strokes her tree. BETH resumes her search.)

BETH. If you don't want your tree to get hit by lightning, you have to keep your promise.

(BILLY enters, unseen, eating an apple. He stares contemptuously at BITTY and BETH.)

BITTY. Ring around my Adult Tree
      Wish someone would marry me.

BETH. Some day I would love to see the world inside your head, child.

BILLY. What are you all doing?

BETH *(jumps up, startled)*. Oh, Billy...nothing.

BILLY. I need money for the movies.

BETH. Well, I don't have any money for that. *(BETH resumes looking for her ring.)*

BITTY *(running around the tree laughing)*. Make a ring with me, Billy Boy! Come on!

BILLY. I told you about calling me that. *(To BETH.)* I walked the brat home today. Ain't that worth two dollars?

BETH. "Isn't," not "ain't." I've got to buy groceries tomorrow. And don't call your sister a brat.

BILLY. Daddy was moaning so I gave him two of those yellow tablets. What about a buck?

BETH. I can't give you what I don't have, Billy. And even if I had it, everything you've done you're supposed to do. I'm not paying you for seeing to your responsibilities.

BILLY *(regards her with intensity)*. Who was that in the Mustang?

BITTY. Mr. Nobody.

BILLY. Why you keep looking on the ground?

BETH. Go inside now. It's going to rain.

BITTY. Ring around my Adult Tree
      Wish someone would marry me.

BILLY. Ring around your what?

BITTY. Ring around my Adult Tree.
      Where will my white wedding be?

BILLY. Stop it, Bratty!

BITTY. I don't have to do what you say, Billy Boy!

BILLY. You want her singing like that?

BETH. Bitty, stop now. *(To BILLY.)* Go inside and wash off that aftershave. Haven't I told you about that? It belongs to your father.

BILLY. He ain't gonna use it.

BITTY. Round and round I smell so sweet
      All the girls will kiss my feet.

BILLY. Keep it up, little girl. You'll be sorry!

BITTY. Round and round you can't catch me
      Kiss the girls and I can see
      Sitting in my Adult Tree.

   (BILLY chases her. She screams.)

BILLY. You ugly brat! You'd better hope I don't catch you.

BETH. Hush now, both of you! Stop.

BILLY. Who I kiss is my business. I catch you spying on me I'm going to smack the tar out of you.

BETH *(grabbing BILLY by the arm)*. And I'll take a belt to you. Just because your daddy can't, doesn't mean that I won't. You'd better not be bringing girls out here, Billy. Keep your mind on your books and finish school. You have to respect your daddy's wishes.

BILLY. Like you? *(Pause.)*

BITTY. Look what I found! *(BITTY holds up the wedding ring. BILLY tries to snatch it, but BITTY holds on.)*

BILLY. Where'd you get that ring?

BETH. Give it to me, Bitty.

BITTY. Under my Adult Tree.

BILLY. You gonna let her run all over the place using that word?

BETH. Call it your "Grown Up Tree," Bitty.

BITTY *(circling the tree and taunting BILLY and BETH)*. Adult Tree! Adult Tree!

BILLY. "Adultery" is a bad word, stupid.

BITTY. It's two words. It isn't cussing, is it, Mama?

BETH. It's not nice to say, honey. Now give Mama the ring. *(BITTY puts the ring on her own finger and sticks her tongue out at BILLY.)*

BITTY. See, it's not cussing! Adult Tree! Adult Tree!

BILLY. Will you tell her what it means?

BETH. She's too young.

BILLY. Think so? Well, one night I caught her out here hugging and kissing that tree! *(BILLY mocks BITTY, who chases him around the tree to make him stop teasing.)* "Oh Raymond, oh Raymond, I love you!"

BITTY. Liar! I hate you, boy! I'm going to tell...I'm going to... *(BETH catches BILLY and BITTY each by the arm.)*

BETH. Hush now! Cut it out, I mean it! *(All three look at one another, breathless, realizing they are on dangerous ground.)*

BITTY. What is "adultree"?

BILLY. It means not faithful.

BITTY. What's "faithful"?

BETH. Enough.

BILLY. "Faithful" means to love somebody like how Mama loves Daddy even though he's sick.

BITTY. Like when you're married?

BILLY. Yeah. Forever.

BITTY. And you can't kiss somebody else?

BILLY. No, stupid.

BITTY. Even if he's a nobody?

BILLY. Look, dummy, if you call this "Adult Tree," it means unfaithful tree. You want to sound like a fool?

BITTY *(circles the tree and chants).*

Ring around my Adult Tree

Will you tell your mystery?

BILLY. I wish you were never born!

BETH. Billy, you take that back!

BILLY. I wish Daddy was better. And I wish Mr. Mustang would die in a car wreck. And I wish I had money for the dang, blasted movies! *(BETH slaps him across the face.)*

BITTY. Don't you hit him or I'll tell! *(BETH looks at both her children. She sits, covers her face and cries. Although the children are glad to see her remorse, they are unnerved by their mother's tears.)*

BETH. I'm sorry. I'm sorry.

BITTY. I didn't mean it, Mama. I won't tell. Please don't cry.

BILLY. Daddy cries too. A lot. Even when the pain ain't there. I hear him at night. Crying because he knows. *(BITTY gives BETH her ring. BETH dries her eyes, puts it on.)* You ain't gonna go away with him, Mama? You ain't gonna...

BETH. I would never ever leave you. I love you, do you understand that?

BITTY. Daddy too?

BETH. Come here, Bitty. You too, Billy, come on. *(BITTY rushes to her mother, BILLY comes slowly. BETH hugs them both and moves slowly in a circle, singing BITTY's tune.)*

Ring around my family
They mean all the world to me.
Ring around my family
What shall be shall always be.

(BETH continues to hum as the three circle slowly and hold onto each other. Fade to black.)

END OF PLAY

OUT OF ORDER

By
CHERIE BENNETT

CHARACTERS

ZOEY, age 14
EVE, about the same age

SETTING: The girls' bathroom of a school.

TIME: The present.

Out of Order

AT RISE: *Rock music plays. Lights up on a school bath-room. There is a full-length mirror and a toilet stall with a large OUT OF ORDER sign on it. ZOEY DEAN, dressed for a school dance, stomps in, livid. She pulls a cell phone from her purse and pushes in a number.*

ZOEY *(into phone).* Heather? It's me... At the school dance. You're never going to believe who... In the john... No, the one in the basement... So I could have *privacy.* Are you ready? *Jason is here...* No, I am not kidding. And he came with Beth Bingham... Yeah, Beth Bingham with the red hair and the really big... I'm *to-tally* serious. So he sees me and his face gets all red, and he goes: "Oh hi, Zoey, I was going to call you." So I go: "Oh hi, Jason, I was going to hold my breath." So then *Beth* goes: "Zoey, could you watch my purse while Ja-son and I dance?" Can you even believe the nerve? So I go: "Sure," like I could care less, because I'm not going to give either one of them the satisfaction of— *(There is a sudden pounding from inside the toilet stall. ZOEY yelps, startled. Into phone:)* Heather? Someone is in here! I'll call you back. *(She drops the phone into her purse. Calling:)* Who's in there? *(Even louder pounding on the door.)* What is your problem? Just open the door! *(A hand appears over the door, points at ZOEY and*

mimes that she should open it.) You want me to open it?
(The hand makes the "Okay" sign. Exasperated:) <u>Fine</u>.

*(ZOEY pulls on the door, it's stuck. She finally yanks it
open. A girl tumbles out, clad in the school's gym uni-
form. Sewn to it is a bikini made of leaves.)*

EVE. Jeez, it took you long enough. *(ZOEY helps the girl
   up and takes in her bizarre outfit.)*
ZOEY. Michael Green told you this was a costume dance,
   didn't he? He pulls that every year. He's such a—
EVE. Who's Michael Green?
ZOEY. You mean you wore that *on purpose*?
EVE. I have a limited wardrobe.
ZOEY. Oh. Sorry. I'm Zoey Dean.
EVE. Yuh, I know. I'm Eve.
ZOEY. Eve what?
EVE. Just "Eve."
ZOEY. Like, just "Madonna" or just "Pink"?
EVE. They totally copied that from me. I would have made
   such an awesome rock star. *(ZOEY decides the girl is
   crazy and backs toward the door.)*
ZOEY. Uh-huh. Well…nice meeting you…uh…Eve.
EVE. Hey, I'm really sorry about what happened with Ja-
   son. *(ZOEY crosses back to EVE.)*
ZOEY. That conversation was *private*.
EVE. I was eavesdropping. Get it? *Eaves*dropping?
ZOEY. *So* not funny. Do you even go to this school?
EVE. …no.
ZOEY. Then you shouldn't be here.
EVE. It's not like I have a choice.
ZOEY. What are you talking about?

EVE *(exasperated)*. Let's review, shall we? I'm *Eve*. Wearing *fig leaves*. Banished from the *Garden*. No *bellybutton*. Do the math. *(Back to the audience, EVE lifts her T-shirt so that ZOEY can see she doesn't have a navel.)*

ZOEY. Whoa, you really don't. That's horrible!

EVE. No kidding. Forget a navel ring.

ZOEY. I mean you're like, deformed. How were you even born?

EVE *(beyond exasperated)*. I *wasn't*. I'm *Eve*.

ZOEY. Please. If you were Eve, you'd be a gazillion years old.

EVE. A gazillion and one on my last birthday, but who's counting?

ZOEY. Then why do you look like a teenager?

EVE. If you're not born, you can't die. Plus, once we got kicked out of the Garden, I didn't get much sun.

ZOEY *(highly dubious)*. Uh-huh. After you got kicked out of the Garden of Eden, you were banished to my school.

EVE. Technically, the *basement* of your school.

ZOEY. So you're telling me Adam's down here, too.

EVE. Yep.

ZOEY. And the snake.

EVE. No. He's crawling around under [name of rival school]. *Much* worse. It's a weird theological space-time-continuum thingie.

ZOEY. You don't really expect me to believe that.

EVE. You want me to explain a weird theological space-time-continuum thingie when you got a C in English?

ZOEY. How'd you know about that?

EVE. You told Heather. I was in the heating vents, listening through the grate.

ZOEY. I thought you were supposed to stay down here.

EVE. Sue me, I have a rebellious streak.

ZOEY. If you could crawl through the vents, why couldn't you crawl *under* the door? *(She indicates the stall door.)*

EVE. There's an order to things. *You* had to invite *me*.

ZOEY. Says who?

EVE. Hey, I don't make the rules. *(EVE catches sight of herself in the mirror and checks out the rear view.)* Do these shorts make my butt look big?

ZOEY *(deadpan sarcasm)*. Don't tell me. Adam only likes supermodels.

EVE. All I'm saying is, in a long-term relationship, you have to make an effort. *(Re her hair.) Hel-*lo. *Rat's* nest. Got a brush I can borrow? *(ZOEY takes a brush from her purse and hands it to EVE, who brushes her hair.)* Thanks. It's a good thing you didn't hand me the cell phone by mistake, huh? It's almost the same size.

ZOEY. Gee, I think I can tell a hairbrush from a cell phone.

EVE. Yeah, but you're not used to carrying a cell. Your parents won't let you have one until you're sixteen. I heard you whining about it to Heather during gym.

ZOEY *(bravado)*. Of course I have a cell. I was just talking on it.

EVE. Speaking of, it's about to ring.

ZOEY. Oh, now we're Psychic Eve? *(The cell phone in ZOEY's purse rings.)* How'd you do that?

EVE. Beth Bingham's mom is a worrier. When Beth goes out, her mom always calls at ten o'clock on the dot, to check in. If Beth doesn't answer, she freaks.

ZOEY. And I care because…?

EVE. Because *you* have Beth's phone.

ZOEY. No I don't.

EVE. Yes you do. You stole it out of her purse. When she went to dance with Jason.

ZOEY *(busted)*. Okay, big deal, so it's her phone. I was only borrowing it.

EVE *(as she hands back ZOEY's hairbrush)*. *This* is borrowing. *(Pointing to the phone in ZOEY's purse.)* *That* is stealing.

ZOEY. Well, she deserved it. Beth Bingham *stole my boyfriend!*

EVE. What is he, a sweater? You can't steal a person.

ZOEY. Yes you can and she did it.

EVE. Oh, I see. *(Beat.)* Hey, let's go streak the dance!

ZOEY. Are you crazy?

EVE. Aw, c'mon. It's okay. It'll be fun!

ZOEY. I'm not running through the dance naked!

EVE. Please-please-please-please-I'll-be-your-best-friend?

ZOEY. I don't want to run through the dance naked, you whack job! I don't just do something because someone asks me to do it.

EVE. Why not?

ZOEY. What do I look like, a zombie? Uh, hello? Free will?

EVE. Too bad Jason the Sweater doesn't have any.

ZOEY *(a light dawns)*. Oh. I get it. You were making a point. Jason doesn't have to be with Beth unless he wants to be with Beth.

EVE. As thieves go, you're quick.

ZOEY. I'm not a thief! I just… She makes me so mad! He was my first boyfriend. We were together for—

EVE. Seven weeks. I heard him that day by the lockers, the first time he asked if you wanted to hang out.

ZOEY. That was so romantic. *(A beat, she darkens.)* I wish I'd never come to this stupid dance. The only reason I came is because my mother made me.

EVE. Forget Jason. The boy's all wrong for you.

ZOEY. How do you know?

EVE. I told you, the vents. He talks about people behind their backs. He cheated on his last math test. And after he—ahem— *(Points to the toilet stall.)* —doesn't wash his hands.

ZOEY *(grossed out)*. Euw. *(The phone in ZOEY's purse rings again.)* I suppose that's Mrs. Bingham again.

EVE. I'm guessing she's about thirty seconds from calling out the National Guard. The woman is a serious overreacter. When Beth didn't make cheerleading, she had to be sedated.

ZOEY. Wild guess: You heard it through the grate.

EVE. Parent's Night. *(A beat. ZOEY eyes her purse guiltily. The cell stops ringing.)*

ZOEY. I never stole anything before. Did you ever steal anything?

EVE. Only one thief in this john, girlfriend. *(She pulls an apple out of the pocket of her gym shorts and takes a bite.)* Bite? *(ZOEY reels in horror.)*

ZOEY *(re the apple)*. That! You stole *that*!

EVE. 'Kay, sometimes an apple is just an apple.

ZOEY. I didn't mean *that* apple. I meant *the* apple.

EVE. The *snake* told me it was okay to eat the apple.

ZOEY. Well, *you* told me it was okay to run through the dance naked!

EVE. That was totally different.

ZOEY. No it wasn't. Take a little responsibility—God knows you're old enough.

EVE *(insulted)*. That's very age-ist of you.

ZOEY. You stole the apple.

EVE. Did not.

ZOEY. Did too.

EVE. Did not.

ZOEY. Did too.

EVE. Fine, fine. I stole the apple! Look, this is not how this is supposed to go. *I'm* supposed to be helping *you*!

ZOEY. You did.

EVE. I did?

ZOEY. Yes. I was wrong to steal Beth's phone.

EVE. Wow. I really did. I rock! So you're returning it?

ZOEY. No. How humiliating would *that* be?

EVE *(wildly frustrated)*. What good is it to realize you were wrong to *steal* the phone if you don't *return* the phone?

ZOEY. Um…none?

EVE. Exactly.

ZOEY. Hey, you didn't return the apple!

EVE. I *ate* it. It wasn't an option!

ZOEY. Like I'm really going to walk up to Beth and go: "Here's your phone. I stole it because I was jealous."

EVE. So take it back upstairs and when no one is looking leave it on the table near the cookies. She'll find it.

ZOEY. Is that cheating?

EVE. Semi.

ZOEY. So would I still be in trouble with…? *(She points skyward.)*

EVE. Like I said, there's an order to things. You're only in trouble with *(points skyward)* if you do it again. *(A beat, as ZOEY considers.)*

ZOEY. Okay, I'll do it.

EVE. Good decision.

ZOEY. Yeah, yeah, free will, yadda, yadda, yadda. *(ZOEY starts to cross to the door, then turns back to EVE.)* Did you ever talk to anyone at this school before?

EVE. No. I stayed in the grates.

ZOEY. So what made you decide to come out and help me?

EVE. Remember when you told me that your mother made you come to the dance? Well...my mother made me come, too.

ZOEY. Your moth— *(A light dawns.)* Oh! You mean... *(She points skyward.)* Your Mother. *(Looking skyward.)* Very cool. *(She gives her hairbrush to EVE. Sincerely:)* To remember me by. Thanks. Really. *(A wistful wave, then ZOEY exits.)*

EVE *(touched)*. You're welcome. *(Rock music from the dance up. A lonely beat—EVE wishes she could join the fun, but can't, because there is an order to things. She rallies, staring at her mirrored reflection, she uses the brush as a microphone and pretends she's a rock star, performing for an adoring crowd.)* Hello, [name of town where play is being performed]! Are you ready to par-tay?

(EVE makes the noise of a cheering crowd, then sings into the brush, rocking out to the music, as the lights fade.)

END OF PLAY

FORK IN THE ROAD

By
Y YORK

CHARACTERS

DESIE, 17, dressed for school

IAN HASKEL, 17, dressed in grease-covered overalls.
Although similar in intelligence, they cope with the
pain of reality differently.

SETTING: Along a moderately traveled road in a
moderately sized town.

TIME: The present. Early morning.

Fork in the Road

AT RISE: *Early morning along the road. DESIE watches cars drive by, waves. Unseen by her, IAN HASKEL stops to watch. She lets a few cars pass, then she waves again.*

IAN HASKEL. I don't get it.

DESIE *(jumps in surprise)*. Ah!

IAN HASKEL. What are you doing?

DESIE. ...Nothing.

IAN HASKEL. Yeah you are—you're waving at cars. I saw you... Do you even know those people?

DESIE. Yeah.

IAN HASKEL. Who are they?

DESIE. ...They're the people who live across the street.

IAN HASKEL. Across what street?

DESIE. Across the street.

IAN HASKEL. Across the street from you?

DESIE. Yeah.

IAN HASKEL. ...The blue car or the white car?

DESIE. What?

IAN HASKEL *(slowly)*. Do the people in the blue car or do the people in the white car live across the street from you?

DESIE. ...Both.

IAN HASKEL *(laughs)*. So what's their name?

DESIE. Jones.

IAN HASKEL. Jones is your name. Desie... You crack me up.

DESIE. I didn't mean to.

IAN HASKEL. So how come you're waving? How come you wave when two cars pass and not when one car passes? *(Silence.)* Come on, spill. *(Silence.)* Hey, I don't care. I'm not going to "turn you in to the authorities."

DESIE. Were you in jail, Ian Haskel?

IAN HASKEL. Jeez, who said that?

DESIE. Nobody. I saw the police car. Then you weren't there anymore.

IAN HASKEL. Don't believe everything you hear.

DESIE. I didn't hear it, I thought it.

IAN HASKEL. Then don't believe everything you think.

DESIE. I don't know how to do that—

IAN HASKEL. Bunch of guys stand up and point their finger, doesn't mean it's true. I was no "danger," no danger to anybody. I punched the wall. That's all who I punched, the wall.

DESIE. ...The hole between the boys' room and the girls' room?

IAN HASKEL *(checks his fist)*. Hurt like crazy. But I didn't punch a guy. None of them were ever in any danger, and they knew it—

DESIE. It was a plaster wall. Very thick.

IAN HASKEL. I wouldn't ever hurt a person, I wouldn't. Mike McKeon wasn't even there. The other guys just told him about it, and he's the one everybody believed...! almost believed him myself, he told such a good story. What are you supposed to do when somebody tells a good story like that on you? Under oath!

DESIE. Mike McKeon is a very good speaker.

IAN HASKEL. See. You believe him, and you didn't even hear what he said.

DESIE. They fixed the hole.

IAN HASKEL. I don't care—I'm not going back. I'm in the real world now. I fix engines. I punch a clock. *(He makes a fist and jabs the air.)* I'm there on time because they pay me to be there on time, which is a better reason to be on time than school reasons, which I never even knew what they were. *(He jabs the air. For the first time, DESIE is a little scared.)*

DESIE. What time is it?

IAN HASKEL. I don't know. It's early yet.

DESIE. I should go to school.

IAN HASKEL. Don't be scared—I told you I didn't punch anybody—

DESIE. No, I just have to get there before the bell.

IAN HASKEL. Yeah? You going to meet somebody? Somebody going to share their morning muffin with you?

DESIE. No muffin.

IAN HASKEL. You going to let somebody copy your homework? Some friend?

DESIE. They look at you if you get there after the bell.

IAN HASKEL. You're not going to miss the bell.

DESIE. What time does your work start?

IAN HASKEL. I just got off. Ian Haskel works while the rest of the world sleeps. Does that make you feel safer? To know that Ian Haskel works while you sleep?

DESIE. I wasn't feeling unsafe—I told you—I don't want to be late for school is all I'm feeling.

IAN HASKEL *(to himself, sad)*. "Don't be late. Don't be early. Don't talk in class. Don't talk in the hall. Be yourself. Fit in with others. Don't pick your nose. Don't pick your friend's nose." All their rules and regulations and stupids. How is a person supposed to cope with all their rules? *(His sadness eases her fear. She tries to cheer him up.)*

DESIE. The rules are good.

IAN HASKEL. Jeez. Which ones?

DESIE. The rules can help you cope. All the lists of rules. They can keep you from making a mistake.

IAN HASKEL. They keep you down, is what they keep you.

DESIE. No, before you do something or say something, let the rules flash, like a blast, in your brain. And then you know what to do, because of the rules.

IAN HASKEL. Not in the real world. The rules don't help in the real world. You want to learn how to deal the real world, get a job, that's where you learn.

DESIE. All I want to learn is physics; a job won't teach me physics.

IAN HASKEL. Sure it will. *(He pulls money out of his wallet.)* The physics of where this comes from. How to get a lot more of this.

DESIE. That's economics. Economics, like physics, is phantom science, depending on belief to exist.

IAN HASKEL. How do you figure that?

DESIE. A dollar is worthless until you believe in its value. You can't see an atom, but you believe it's there.

IAN HASKEL. ...Economics, okay, maybe, but physics is solid, not phantom. "An object in motion tends to remain in motion," whether you believe it or not.

DESIE. Not that kind of physics. The molecular kind. You have to believe that all of the molecules that make up your dollar bills are going to remain in place relative to one another. If the molecules disperse, your wallet could be empty when you look in there.

IAN HASKEL *(amused)*. It's a good thing you're studying physics, Desie. Your theories need a lot of work. *(She turns away from his rebuke and waves as cars pass.)* They live across the street, too? Come on, tell me what you're doing. *(Brief pause.)* Do you want me to stay and talk to you or not?

DESIE. I can't decide.

IAN HASKEL. Oh, yeah. Because you got so many people that talk to you, that are nice to you, that are dying to hear your theories on physics, that you can just toss one of them away. Right?

DESIE. ...No.

IAN HASKEL. Yeah, no. So if you want me to stick around and talk to you...be nice to you...be friends with you...you have to tell me about the waving.

DESIE *(amazed)*. You're going to be friends with me?

IAN HASKEL. If you tell me about the waving, I am. Otherwise I'll go away, and you can be all by yourself again.

DESIE. Okay, okay. *(Whispers.)* My arm needs to wave. When I'm near the road, it takes all my willpower to keep my arm from waving. But it upsets them when you wave at them—the people in the cars. They turn around and drive up to you and say "why are you waving?" So I do this: I wait until there are two cars close together. Then I let my arm wave and I put my glance between the two cars, that way the people in each car think I'm waving at the other car... Also before I wave again, I make sure all the cars-that-might-have-seen-me-wave-already have driven by. *(Brief pause.)* I used to squeeze my toes together. My toes needed to squeeze, and I could squeeze them any time any place—nobody would know—somebody could be standing right next to me. But then my feet got cramps. That's when I started to wave. Waving cured my squeezing. *(Silence, as he contemplates her. Then, a confession.)*

IAN HASKEL. I need to squeeze, too. My hand into a fist. It's a big need.

DESIE *(small waves at him, then)*. Now? Do you need to squeeze now?

IAN HASKEL. ...No. *(Slightly surprised.)* I don't seem to need it now.

DESIE. I need to wave all the time.

IAN HASKEL. No, not all the time. Just when it starts to...when I start to...

DESIE. Unravel?

IAN HASKEL. Yeah.

DESIE. Disperse?

IAN HASKEL. Yeah!

DESIE. All your molecules start to escape?

IAN HASKEL *(nodding)*. And I need to rein them back, so I squeeze. Hold everything in.

DESIE. So it can't escape.

IAN HASKEL. Yeah... You get it.

DESIE. Well, yeah. It's physics.

IAN HASKEL. You really get it. *(A silent moment of connection. She is happy throughout the following exchange.)* You're like some kind of antidote to my squeezing.

DESIE. I'm an antidote?

IAN HASKEL. Yeah, a looseness. And not only that, you glow. There's this light around you, a halo.

DESIE. Aura. Made from escaping molecules.

IAN HASKEL. Yeah. Do I have one?

DESIE *(looks to see)*. No. Squeezing is working. No molecules escaping.

IAN HASKEL. I'm not squeezing now. I should have an aura, too.

DESIE. Maybe you're doing a mental squeezing. Keeping all the molecules in place with your belief.

IAN HASKEL. I'm not doing that. I should have one.

DESIE. Nothing there.

IAN HASKEL. Look harder. *(Brief pause.)* You don't see one? An aura around my head?

DESIE. No. Just a head.

IAN HASKEL. Are you sure?

DESIE. I'm sure.

IAN HASKEL. ...You could have said you saw one. You could have said one was there. *(Her happiness is punctured by his disappointment.)*

DESIE. How could I have said that?

IAN HASKEL. You just could have. You could have said, "yes I see it. It's very little but it's definitely there."

DESIE. But it wouldn't have been true.

IAN HASKEL. But it would have been nice!

DESIE *(really asking)*. Is that allowed?

IAN HASKEL. Is what allowed?

DESIE. Can it be not true if it's nice?

IAN HASKEL. It's allowed. What? You got some list of rules bursting in your brain telling you not to be nice?

DESIE. I might have misunderstood. The rule. *(Pause.)* Is it too late? Too late to see your aura?

IAN HASKEL. Yeah. It's too late. *(He starts to leave. She gasps at him and points at his head.)* What? What's wrong?

DESIE. Little lights. Little colored lights. Escaping.

IAN HASKEL. ...Yeah?

DESIE. Thousands—millions.

IAN HASKEL. That many, huh?

DESIE. And dancing—a dancing glowing.

IAN HASKEL. ...You don't have to overdo it.

DESIE. No! Really! Really! Little lights.

(The happy end.)

END OF PLAY

GET

By
JAMES DeVITA

CHARACTERS

JESSE, a boy of about 14 or 15
KEVIN, his brother, high energy, mid- to late 20s
CLAUDIA, their sister, about 17

SETTING: A lawyer's office.

TIME: Now.

Get

AT RISE: *A lawyer's office. JESSE is sitting on a bench listening to a portable CD player. He wears loose-fitting clothes, a wild-colored tie-dyed T-shirt and a funky loose-knit cap. His eyes are closed as he sways back and forth listening to his music. KEVIN is on his cell phone mid-conversation. He is dressed extremely smart in a suit and tie, professional but very hip.*

KEVIN. I want champagne. Yeah. No, no, champagne the color. It's a color. What are you talking about? Every exec in the building has one. *(To JESSE.)* You believe this guy? *(Into phone.)* No, it's nothing like that, it's kind of, you know, it's kind of...it's champagne-y—it's like a light tan, like a kinda light gold...gold-ish, kinda light tan, you know? *(JESSE starts making percussive sounds with his mouth. He will do this wherever appropriate whenever he speaks his hip-hop.)* Like champagne. Yeah. That's why they call it that.

JESSE. Champagne be the name say the man on the train...

KEVIN *(into phone)*. Look, okay, okay—stop! Stop! Look out your window.

JESSE. His face lookin' pained as he tries to explain... *(Percussive sounds.)*

KEVIN *(overlapping percussive sounds)*. Just, just look out
   the—

JESSE. ...this game named fame... *(Percussive sounds.)*

KEVIN. Jesse, please?

JESSE. ...it's a shame it's so lame... *(Percussive sounds.)*

KEVIN *(into phone)*. You looking?

JESSE. ...it's drain on the brain... *(Percussive sounds.)*

KEVIN *(giving JESSE a look, but into the phone)*. The
   company parking lot—you looking at it? Okay, good—
   look to your right. See where the VIPs park? The president, vice president? Look at their cars. That's champagne. Yeah. Get me one. *(Shaking his head in disgust
   and dialing another number on his phone as he looks at
   his watch. JESSE continues soft percussive sounds, en-
   tertaining himself.)* These interns working for me are
   about this *(holds up a pen)* smart. I wheeler-dealed a
   company car with my new contract. Two of the guys in
   marketing had one. I figure why should they get one and
   not me, right?—management went for it. Hey, give me a
   break with the rapping, would you, Jess?

JESSE. It's true what I do may be voodoo à la you but the
   reason for ma' teasin' is you gotta getta clue, get a clue,
   get clue, gotta gotta getta clue.

KEVIN. C'mon already—

JESSE. Don't be a moo in a zoo.

KEVIN. Make yourself useful and help me find a phonebook in here.

JESSE. Be the bro that can-do.

KEVIN. I need a— *(Into his phone.)* Hi. Yeah, it's me.

JESSE *(softly, to himself)*. The bro that can-do- *(Rapid-fire
   percussive.)* -do, do, do, do, do, do, do.

KEVIN. I'm going to be late. *(Louder. Looking for a phonebook.)* LATE. Yeah, I'm going to have to get a ride. *(Of phone.)* Great, this thing is dying. *(Into phone.)* What? I can't hear you.

(CLAUDIA enters. She is wearing helmet, sunglasses and a backpack.)

KEVIN. I'm going to call you on the land line. Yeah, call you right back. *(He uses a phone on the desk. To CLAUDIA.)* Hey.

CLAUDIA *(doesn't acknowledge KEVIN. She speaks to JESSE)*. Hey.

JESSE *(high-fiving CLAUDIA)*. I weigh what you say and I lay the trey—hey. *(She sits on the bench.)*

KEVIN *(into phone)*. Yeah, it's me. Hold on. *(Finding and giving phonebook to JESSE.)* Jesse, could you look me up a limo service— *(Into phone.)* What? You gotta talk louder.

CLAUDIA *(to JESSE of the music he is listening to)*. What? *(JESSE holds up the CD cover. CLAUDIA takes it, removes her sunglasses and examines it.)*

KEVIN *(into phone)*. Can you hear me? I can't hear you.

CLAUDIA *(to JESSE, handing the CD back)*. Are they here yet? *(JESSE shakes his head "no.")*

KEVIN. Hey, Jess, do me a favor and look up a— *(Into phone.)* What? No, just stay where you are; I'm not going to get dropped off like some car-pooling office goon. I'm looking up a— *(JESSE gives him the phonebook having looked up the number. KEVIN grabs it.)* Thanks. *(Into phone.)* Got a pen? Okay, call this number and get me a limo: 555-XXXX. *(Spelling it out slower.)* 555-

XXXX. All right? Good. Have them meet me here after one-thirty. Yeah. Okay. Okay. Yeah. 'Bye. *(Sits between CLAUDIA and JESSE. JESSE takes off his headphones. All looking straight ahead.)* It's a wonder. You know that? Working with people like this? It's a wonder we've come this far. The human race. We're doomed. I actually think we're doomed. *(Pause.)* "Doom on you." Wasn't that from—did you see that movie? We took the kids to it? The one with the penguins? The extinct penguins?

JESSE. Your song is all wrong—they be the dodo, you bozo.

KEVIN. What?

CLAUDIA *(coldly)*. They were dodo birds. Penguins aren't extinct. We still have penguins.

JESSE. Who be chillin' on their...ten-fins...on the ice where it's nice while I'm mining for the rhyming.

KEVIN *(ignoring JESSE)*. I was just saying. It was a movie. Excuse me. *(Pause. To CLAUDIA.)* You're late.

CLAUDIA. So?

KEVIN *(beat. Of helmet)*. What's with the...?

CLAUDIA. It protects my head.

KEVIN. Don't be wise.

JESSE. Rhapsodize.

CLAUDIA. I biked here, okay?

KEVIN. Should have took the bus with Jess. What's the matter, you don't believe in mass transit either?

CLAUDIA *(angry)*. Is it any of your business, Kevin!? Like you could even understand what I believe in or don't anyway. Have you ever cared about anything I've ever done in my life—ever?! Just leave me alone, all right?!

KEVIN. Fine. I was just asking—forget it.

CLAUDIA. I don't even want to be here!

KEVIN. Hey, I don't want to be here either! I've got better things to do.

CLAUDIA. Then leave!

KEVIN. You leave!

JESSE. Yo, this spill is gettin' ill, Mrs. Sister, Mr. Brother, let us mill a chill-pill 'fore we hurt one another.

KEVIN *(to CLAUDIA)*. I'm not the reason we're here to-day, you are.

CLAUDIA. This is my fault?

KEVIN. You're the one who started whining in the first place. There wouldn't even be a lawyer involved if you hadn't gone and—

CLAUDIA. Hey, you're the one who went in and snuck off with everything.

KEVIN. I didn't sneak off with anything!

JESSE. Denial for a while—you can't wheedle through the needle, though a camel is a mammal, it will—

KEVIN. Stop it, Jesse!

CLAUDIA *(overlapping KEVIN's last line)*. Oh, please, Kevin. You get the car 'cause you're older—which you sold to buy that monstrosity you've got now—you got the computers 'cause you're in business—okay, I can maybe understand that—but then you get the desk, the TV, the stereo? All his music? The pictures. We show up one day and it's all gone! That's not sneaking off? It wasn't yours to take in the first place, the divorce wasn't final so everything still all belongs to Mom.

KEVIN. She didn't want anything to do with it! She told me so! She wasn't going to go over there and go through all his stuff. And you said yourself you didn't want anything anyway! You said it right in front of him. *(Sarcastic. Mocking her.)* "I'm never going to be like him. I don't care about things." You don't remember saying that? Jesse—you were there—did she say that?

JESSE. Not to dis ya, my sista, but the shot didn't miss ya—he talking true smack, yo, he gotcha on that.

CLAUDIA. I don't care about that stuff, Kevin—take it, take it all and cram it in the back of your shamelessly obscenely, disgusting, wasteful, gross Humvee—just because you can—and do whatever you want with it.

KEVIN. My car's in the shop.

CLAUDIA. Great, make a joke—I'm not talking about that stuff, Kevin.

KEVIN. Then what are you talking about?

CLAUDIA. I'm talking about things that don't mean anything to you—and they did to me. Things that don't have any immediate market value? Okay? If you can understand that.

KEVIN. What would you do with his stuff anyway? Why should you have it? You were fine till you saw I had a few things—then all of a sudden everything starts having sentimental value.

CLAUDIA. A few things?! You cleaned the place out.

JESSE. Which is reason for some pout, yo, this thief in the night causin' grief in the light.

KEVIN *(threatening JESSE)*. I'm gonna give you some grief in about two seconds!

JESSE *(turns away. Quietly searching for a rhyme)*. Two seconds?...moo less-ons...goo ess-ence...blue penguins? *(Shakes his head "no" on the last one.)*

CLAUDIA *(to KEVIN)*. Didn't you think I might want something? Anything?

KEVIN. Why would I think that?

CLAUDIA. You are such a loser.

KEVIN. No, really, why? 'Cause you two were so close?

CLAUDIA. Shut up.

KEVIN. I'm sorry, when was the last time you talked to him? How many times did you visit him in the hospital?

CLAUDIA. That's not the point.

KEVIN. And what would be the point?

CLAUDIA. You could have asked. You could have asked me, Kevin.

KEVIN. And you could have acted like an adult. Mom went to see him more than you.

CLAUDIA. He could have acted like an adult and not left us for some... You have no right to all his things.

KEVIN. And you do?! I'd rather send it to Goodwill than you should have it.

CLAUDIA. That's real mature—if you can't have it then nobody can. You don't care. It's not about Dad and me. You're not trying to punish me, you just don't want anyone to have more than you—of anything.

JESSE. The wind can't be pinned, 'n the breeze can't be seized.

KEVIN. Enough, Jess.

CLAUDIA. So long as you have more toys than anyone else, you're happy, aren't you, Kevin? You always get what you want, don't you? Even if you have to take it.

KEVIN. I get what I want because I work hard for it and I deserve it. Not like you.

JESSE. The labor is a faker, when you caper for a vapor.

KEVIN *(turning on JESSE)*. And not like you!

JESSE. Whoa, Fu Manchu! She and me we not the hated, we're all here related. You only started crude, now you gettin' ruder, dude! We gotta rise above it 'cause the killer is to covet, so, my sister and my brother—

KEVIN. Talk like a human being, Jesse! And don't dude me, okay? Nobody says dude anymore—and what are you doing here dressed like that!? You look like you fell into a tie-dye machine run amuck—you're not retro, you're embarrassing. *(To CLAUDIA.)* And you, you look like...what are you dressed for? It's like Halloween around here. I don't believe you two. Show some respect.

CLAUDIA. Show some respect? *(Quiet, to KEVIN. She's done talking.)* You're a jerk.

JESSE *(shakes his head as he puts his headphones back on)*. Man...doom on you, dude...doom on you...

KEVIN. Great. *(An uncomfortable pause. KEVIN looks at his watch.)* I can't wait here all day.

CLAUDIA. So go.

KEVIN. Some of us have jobs, you know.

CLAUDIA. Go!

KEVIN. I will.

CLAUDIA. Good. *(Silence. No one goes anywhere.)*

JESSE *(starting softly, gets up and performs his hip-hop fully, vocally supplying his own percussion sounds)*. This quiet is a riot, and this war is a bore, can you tell me what it's for, why I's just to get more. Yo, it's just to get a get, get a get, get a get, and I gotta getta get—get a get a what? *(Beat.)* Don't matter what the what or the crave or the wish or the name or the claim 'cause the get is the same. It's anything you got, if the other's it's not—didn't even feel a lack—now I want that back! I want that back! Acquire, desire, it's such a quagmire, stuck grudging your neighbors trying to get their get that they got with their labors. So, sister and brother, yo, discuss at your leisure, while we wait for the judge, think measure for measure... *(Percussive sounds.)* ...think measure for measure... *(Percussive sounds.)* ...gettin' pleasure from treasure... *(Percussive sounds.)* ...is this hate our fate?... *(Percussive sounds.)* ...that's the big debate... *(Percussive sounds.)* ...is the got worth the get... *(Percussive sounds.)* ...is the got worth the get... *(Percussive sounds.)* ...is the got worth the get... *(Percussive sounds.)*

(JESSE trails off, making quieter sounds of percussion until he eventually sits back where he was and retreats again into his music. CLAUDIA puts her sunglasses back on. KEVIN tries his cell phone again and holds it to his ear. They all three are looking straight out. Black-out.)

END OF PLAY

DIRECTOR'S NOTES

DIRECTOR'S NOTES

DIRECTOR'S NOTES

DIRECTOR'S NOTES

DIRECTOR'S NOTES